The Allyn & Bacon Editing Exercises

Anna Ingalls
Southwestern College

Dan Moody
Southwestern College

Longman

New York   San Francisco   Boston
London   Toronto   Sydney   Tokyo   Singapore   Madrid
Mexico City   Munich   Paris   Cape Town   Hong Kong   Montreal

Contents

Identifying Verbs

Directions: Underline the verbs in the following paragraph. In the space above each, label the verb *A* (action) or *L* (linking). Check to be sure that you have underlined the whole verb.

                                                                          L
Example: The Statue of Liberty in New York Harbor <u>is</u> the first thing that many

                   A
immigrants <u>see</u>.

    Immigrants have made many important contributions to the United States of America. The Statue of Liberty honors them for their contributions. Even today, more than fifteen percent of the residents of New York were born outside of the United States. Over the years, New York City has indeed been a city of opportunity and success for many immigrants. However, others live in poverty. New York City is the cultural capital of the United States. More book publishers and theater companies can be found in New York than in any other city in America. Several of the nation's most famous art museums are also located in New York. On the other hand, many thousands of New Yorkers live in substandard housing. In fact, almost one million new Yorkers receive income assistance from the government. Some of the richest and poorest people in our country are among the residents of the most famous part of the city, Manhattan.

Distinguishing Between the Simple and the Complete Subject

Directions: Underline the complete subject, and circle the simple subject in each sentence below.

Example: <u>My first apartment</u> made me feel both proud and embarrassed.

A struggling graduate student with a limited income can't afford to live in luxury. In my case, a modest studio apartment in an old, run-down building was my home. The bathroom and kitchen were each about the size of a small closet, with barely enough room to turn around. In the kitchen hung cheap-looking curtains with a bright aqua floral print. Matching panels of the same floral material covered the front of the open cupboards. An ugly green couch with black arms and a sagging brown recliner didn't coordinate with anything else in the apartment. However, both of them were comfortable places to study. A cheap coffee table with several ring marks from glasses completed my odd collection of mismatched furniture. Visiting friends or relatives never approved of my apartment. According to my mother, it looked dreary and depressing. Still, coming home to my own little place in the world made me feel good.

Recognizing Subjects and Verbs

Directions: In each sentence, underline the complete subject, and circle the simple subject. Double underline each verb, verb phrase, or compound verb.

Example: <u>Your first job</u> <u>can teach</u> you many skills that <u>you</u> <u>will need</u> later in life.

My first real job was as a stock clerk at the nearby TG&Y variety store. I had never worked in a business before. Therefore, the store manager's goal was to bring me up to speed on the "rules" of the retail world. The first rule was to arrive slightly early every day.   With all employees there early, the manager didn't worry about not having enough help. The second rule of the store was not to sit down while counting stock or dusting shelves. Rules three and four prohibited gossip about the other employees and customers. The fifth rule was to volunteer for another job as soon as one job was finished.   In addition to these rules, the manager was able to include many other things in my training. Stock rotation and customer assistance might not have been the most exciting skills to learn. However, everything about my experience at the TG&Y would help me in my later jobs.

Correcting Fragments with Missing Subjects or Verbs

Directions: Underline the fragments in the following paragraph. Then correct the fragments by adding an appropriate subject or verb, or both, or revising an incorrect verb form.

Example: Television ~~making~~ *makes* it possible to share events around the world.

When a tragedy occurs anywhere in the world, millions of viewers sharing it simultaneously. For example, television brought the untimely deaths of both Princess Diana and John F. Kennedy, Jr., directly into our living rooms. Wept with the royal family and the British people as we watched the funeral cortège and memorial services for "the People's Princess." Photographs of her childhood, her marriage to Prince Charles, and her many activities on behalf of charitable causes. Elton John's heartfelt song "Candle in the Wind" bringing tears to our eyes. John F. Kennedy, Jr., like Princess Diana, an idol and inspiration for an entire generation. Some television stations to broadcast continuously as the Coast Guard searched for the missing plane piloted by JFK, which had disappeared en route to Martha's Vineyard. Also carried his wife, Carolyn Bessette Kennedy, and her sister, Lauren Bessette. When it was finally determined that that the plane had gone down and there were no survivors, shared the sadness of the Kennedy family, who once again had been struck by tragedy. Images like these will remain in our minds forever.

Correcting Phrase Fragments and Subordinate Clause Fragments

Directions: Underline the fragments in the following passage. Then, on a separate piece of paper, revise the passage by correcting the fragments.

Example: Some people have trouble expressing their feelings. <u>And their needs.</u>

Corrected: *Some people have trouble expressing their feelings and their needs.*

Many colleges offer personal development classes. Which often include something called assertiveness training. Unfortunately, the term "assertive" is often misunderstood. Some people think that being assertive means the same thing. As being aggressive. However, assertiveness and aggressiveness are actually very different. A person who is aggressive tends to be argumentative. And forceful. An aggressive person often intimidates or offends people. Trying to force his opinions on others. On the other hand, when you are assertive. You stand up for your rights in a non-threatening manner. To be assertive, you should clearly state. What you want. It is important to speak up for yourself. And not let other people bully you into going along with their ideas. For example, do not agree to drive a friend to work every day. Or keep his pet rabbits for a month. Unless you really want to do these things. By learning to assert yourself without becoming aggressive. You will feel better about yourself. In addition, you will gain the respect of others.

When finally reached the far side of the crater and began our ascent. I was

exhausted. But also a feeling of satisfaction and awe.

Combining Simple Sentences to Create Complex Sentences

Directions: Rewrite the following paragraph, using subordinating conjunctions and relative pronouns to create complex sentences where they are appropriate. You may choose to leave some sentences as they are.

Example: We had several views of Mount Rainier. Every view was spectacular.

Using Subordination: *Every view **that** we had of Mount Rainier was spectacular.*

We first sighted the snow-capped peak of Mount Rainier. We were still miles away. The clouds had hidden the peak from view for several days. They had finally disappeared. Even from a distance, Mount Rainier dominated the countryside. It is 14,410 feet above sea level. We drove through forests and country towns. They looked as if they belonged in the Old West. Mt. Rainier would sometimes disappear from view and then reappear, larger than ever. The road descended into a valley. It began to follow the winding route of the chalky gray Carbon River. It is fed by glaciers high on the mountainside. The road began to ascend and gradually became a narrow trail. We looked across pine-forested valleys and foothills immediately in front of us. We saw the huge volcanic slopes and rocky cliffs of Mt. Rainier, and we stared in awe at the ancient, lofty peak. It was such a magnificent sight.

Combining Simple Sentences to Create Compound Sentences

Directions: Rewrite the following paragraph, using coordinating conjunctions, conjunctive adverbs, or semicolons to create compound sentences where they are appropriate. You may choose to leave some sentences as they are.

Example: Washington is the only state named after a president. Many cities and counties are named after presidents.

Using Coordination: *Washington is the only state named after a president; however, many cities and counties are named after presidents.*

The state of Washington has a landscape that is full of contrasts. To the west, Washington is bordered by the Pacific Ocean. There are many large islands, waterways, and rivers. This area is famous for salmon and trout fishing. Near the coast, there are evergreen rain forests. The middle of the state consists of a high mountain range. These mountains have many snow-covered peaks. Many people come to Washington to ski every year. Hikers, rock climbers, and mountain bikers enjoy the many recreational opportunities in these mountains. There are quite a few inactive volcanoes in this range. One volcano, Mount St. Helens, erupted in 1980. The western part of the state is very wet. East of the Cascade Mountains, there are dry, treeless plains. This area is very productive. Irrigation turns the dry land into rich farmland.

Using Coordination and Subordination

Directions: Rewrite the following paragraph to emphasize ideas, to show connections among ideas, and to make the writing smooth. Change some of the simple sentences to compound and complex sentences. You may choose to leave some sentences as they are.

Example: There are many volcanoes in the continental United States. Most of them are inactive. Some of them still erupt at rare intervals.

*There are many volcanoes in the continental United States, **and** most of them are inactive; **nevertheless**, a few of them may still erupt at rare intervals.*

Mount St. Helens is located in the State of Washington in the Pacific Northwest of the United States. There was a violent eruption there on May 18, 1980. More than fifty people died. Tremendous damage occurred in the surrounding area. A wall of steam, water, and ash rolled down the mountain. It flattened trees and killed every living thing it touched. The eruption was over. Mount St. Helens was more than one thousand feet shorter. Another volcano in California, Oregon, Washington, or another state may erupt in the not-too-distant future. It would have a far-reaching effect. A big eruption in the West could leave an inch or more of ash as far east as Boston and New York City. No one knows when one of these volcanoes might erupt again.

Recognizing Comma Splices and Run-ons

Directions: The following paragraph contains several comma splices and run-on sentences. Put an * in front of any comma splice or run-on, and insert a / where one sentence should end and the next should begin.

Example: *Computers have become a part of our daily lives,/ we rely on them for education, business, and entertainment.

During the last few years, more and more people have come to rely on computers the number of Internet users is increasing every day. By 1999, there were 92 million Internet users in North America. Some people use the Internet for business or educational purposes, others use it mainly for entertainment. Entertainment possibilities include meeting people in chat rooms, playing games online, and downloading pictures of your favorite sports figures or movie stars. Another possibility is cyber-dating, keep in mind, however, that meeting a "cyber-date" in real life could be dangerous. People you meet online may not always tell the truth about themselves. For example, someone who claims to be twenty-five may actually turn out to be fifteen or forty-five unethical individuals may also lie about other things, such as their job, their physical appearance, or their marital status. Although you may be lucky enough to get acquainted online with people who become lifelong friends, it is important to be cautious.

Correcting Comma Splices and Run-ons 1

Directions: First, identify comma splices and run-ons in the following passage by putting an * in front of each one. Then correct the comma splices and run-ons by adding a coordinating conjunction, a subordinating conjunction, a conjunctive adverb, a semicolon, or a period. In some cases, more than one solution is possible.

Example: *Commercials are big business, large companies will pay millions of dollars to place their ads on highly rated television programs.

Corrected: Commercials are big business; large companies will pay millions of dollars to place their ads on highly rated television programs.

A talking Chihuahua tries to persuade us to eat at a certain fast food restaurant, frogs croak their approval of a certain brand of beer. TV commercials use any technique they can to capture viewers' attention their goal is to persuade consumers to buy their products. Many commercials appeal to younger viewers they are the prime target of a large number of advertisers. Although teenagers don't have unlimited funds, they have a great deal of influence on household spending, advertisers hope they will form lifetime shopping habits. The same brands that they buy and use as teenagers are likely to remain their favorite brands ten or twenty years from now. Of course, there is another possibility a competitor's clever ad may persuade them to try another brand.

Correcting Comma Splices and Run-ons 2

Directions: First, identify comma splices and run-ons in the following passage by putting an * in front of each one. Then correct the comma splices and run-ons by adding a coordinating conjunction, a subordinating conjunction, a conjunctive adverb, a semicolon, or a period. In some cases, more than one solution is possible.

Example: *Most of us live fast-paced lives, learning to manage our time well is important.

Corrected: Most of us live fast-paced lives, **so** learning to manage our time well is important.

The ability to plan is an important skill it will help you succeed in college as well as in your job. Whenever a major project or assignment is announced, time should be set aside to complete it. First, you should figure out the steps or stages in the process, then estimate how long each step will take. It is important to allow plenty of time, preferably over a period of several days. For example, if your history instructor announces that there will be a test on chapters 6, 7, 8, and 9 next Friday, you should plan a reading and study schedule for yourself. An ideal plan would include 2-3 hours per chapter for a thorough reading additional time for review and study should also be included. You should plan to spend a few hours reviewing your class notes. Most students can also benefit from forming a study group with other classmates group members should schedule specific hours for intensive study sessions. By planning an adequate amount of time for each of these steps, you will

avoid a stressful last-minute rush. Similarly, the ability to use effective planning

techniques can help you be successful at your job.

Basic Subject-Verb Agreement

Directions: The following paragraph contains a number of errors in subject-verb agreement with special subjects, including collective subjects, compound subjects, indefinite pronouns, and others. Cross out the errors and write the correct verb form above the line.

gives
Example: A group of returning students ~~give~~ the orientation each year.

First-time college students like my brother Jake often has a hard time connecting with other students, especially if they commutes to classes every day. He says that there are usually only time to say a quick hello to classmates before his first class get underway, and for the rest of the day, he is constantly on the go, running from class to class. "Everyone need friends," I told him, "and you are no exception." When I asked him why he doesn't speak to the other students in class, he told me, "I am taking advanced classes, and I need to concentrate on the lectures. For example, mathematics are difficult enough when I give it my full attention, and I don't want to risk getting a bad grade in any of my classes." I then suggested a group activity or club, and he told me that a sports team offer a lot of opportunities to meet other guys, but that he was more interested in meeting members of the opposite sex. "Hmmm," I replied, "then a club or other student organization are just what you are looking for." He finally decided that the Fencing Team and the Environmental Club was possibilities. Both of them include a mix of males and females, so I think he will make friends there. As I told him, four years of college are a long time to feel lonely.

Maintaining Agreement with Indefinite Pronouns, Collective Nouns, and Compound Subjects

Directions: Correct all errors in subject-verb agreement. Most of the agreement errors involve indefinite pronouns, collective nouns, or compound subjects. For each error, draw a line through the incorrect verb, and write the correct form above the line.

helps
Example: A supportive group to belong to ~~help~~ a person feel secure.

Nobody want to be a misfit. Everyone need to feel accepted and valued by others. Without that kind of group acceptance, one is likely to lead a lonely, isolated life. A group offer a sense of security and belonging to all its members. Family or friends provides an extremely important group identity for most people. For example, sisters, brothers, and cousins all feels a sense of belonging to the same family and generally remains loyal to the family unit. In return, the family also give them something. A set of values, acceptance, and unconditional love are a few of the most important benefits. Many people is members of several different groups in addition to their family. A sports team offer many of the same rewards, and so do a club or a Scout troop. Unfortunately, some young people today find their group identity in a gang. To them, a gang seem almost like a family. Although none of us can choose the family that we are born into, all of us needs to choose our other group memberships wisely.

Correcting Subject-Verb Agreement Errors

Directions: Correct all errors in subject-verb agreement. Draw a line through the incorrect verb, and write the correct form above the line.

gain
Example: With distance learning, people ~~gains~~ an education without even leaving home.

Because of the Internet, new ways of teaching and learning has evolved. The term "distance learning" refer to accessing information with a computer and modem from sources that may be located thousands of miles away. Many colleges and other organizations now includes distance learning courses in their curriculum. Some people even earns their college degrees through distance learning, without ever being on the campus of the university. The distance learning teacher usually post information for students to access and sometimes gives a real-time lecture—in written form, of course. Interactive communication between teacher and students are also possible. A chat room with restricted access works well for this purpose. Special message boards also allows students to post questions. Students uses e-mail to send in their written assignment and also receive comments from the instructor by e-mail. Although some people complains that distance learning lacks the personal touch, others like it very much. It may be the perfect solution for some individuals who do not have access to a nearby college or university.

Using *Will* to Show Future Time

Directions: In the following paragraph, change the present tense verbs to show future time using *will*.

will host
Example: Chicago ~~hosts~~ one of the groups of Brazilian teachers.

In the near future, four groups of Brazilian teachers of English as a Foreign Language come to various cities in the United States. They observe classes of English as a Second Language, tour language laboratories, and share information about situations and methods with U.S. teachers. A few months later, four groups of teachers from the United States travel to Brazil on a reciprocal visit. They visit English and Portuguese classes in Brazil. The trip is in summer, so it does not interfere with the teachers' own classes. The Fulbright Foundation sponsors both of these upcoming visits in order to promote increased international understanding and cooperation. This visit is an incredible opportunity for teachers to learn from teachers and students in another country.

Using the Past Tense

Directions: In the following paragraph, change the present tense verbs to the past tense.

worked
Example: Six people ~~work~~ several hours to clean up after the picnic.

To get ready for the big potluck picnic, we reserve the picnic area at the park

three months in advance. At 11:00 on the day of the picnic, we pull into the park,

park the car, and unload the canopy, chairs, and the food that we prepare that

morning. Many of our friends and their families arrive soon afterwards. Then we

enter the line and help ourselves to some of the many dishes that people had

prepared, which include some of my favorite foods: fried chicken, macaroni, beans,

watermelon, brownies, and chocolate chip cookies. After we ate and visit with some

friends, the younger children enjoy snow cones, and later, jump on the trampoline.

The older children play softball, and the parents mostly just talk and share a relaxing

afternoon together.

Using the Perfect Tenses

Directions: In the following paragraph, some of the present tense verbs are underlined. Change the present tense verbs to the present perfect, past perfect, or future perfect forms, as appropriate.

has improved
Example: Adding compost to the soil this year ~~improves~~ it a lot.

Before last March, it is several years since I <u>plant</u> a vegetable garden. For several years before that, I was too busy, or too disorganized, to plant a garden. This year, I <u>plant</u> only squash and tomatoes so far, but the results already <u>impress</u> me. The squash <u>is</u> ready for several weeks already, and we <u>pick</u> a lot of squash. I planted the tomatoes late this year, so they are not ripe yet. By next month, we <u>savor</u> our first ripe, homegrown tomatoes, and we are very much looking forward to that wonderful, sweet-tart flavor. I recommend gardening to everyone, even if you only have room for one cherry tomato plant in a container. If you never <u>garden</u> before, you might be surprised at how satisfying it is to grow your own vegetables.

Using Irregular Verbs Correctly

Directions: For each verb in parentheses, use the correct past tense form or past participle form, as appropriate. Include a helping verb if necessary. Cross out the verb in parentheses and write the correct form above the line.

became
Example: The radio ~~(become)~~ a popular form of family entertainment in the 1920s.

Many authors (write) about the 1920s, including F. Scott Fitzgerald. Although Fitzgerald's book *The Great Gatsby* (be) not popular when it was first published in 1925, in recent years many thousands of college students (read) it. Some people say that they (know) nothing about the 1920s before reading *The Great Gatsby.* However, afterward, they (understand) something about the lavish and often carefree lifestyle of the rich during that era.

At the beginning of the decade, in 1920, the 18th Amendment (go) into effect, establishing Prohibition nationwide. This (mean) that anyone who produced or (sell) alcoholic beverages was breaking the law. Organized crime (take) advantage of the situation, and bootleggers (make) alcohol available to those who could afford it.

The 1920s (become) known as "the Roaring Twenties." Many people (be) in a free-spirited mood after the end of The Great War (World War I) and (seek) thrills or excitement in various ways. In 1927, Charles Lindbergh (make) history when he (fly) across the Atlantic in 33 1/2 hours, and people (see) him as a hero. Another

popular hero who (rise) to fame in the 1920s was Babe Ruth, baseball's "Sultan of

Swat."

Correcting Errors with *Can / Could, Will / Would,* and Forms of *to Be*

Directions: Correct errors in the use of *can* and *could, will* and *would,* and the forms of the verb *to be.* Cross out the incorrect forms and write the correct forms above the line.

can
Example: Nowadays we ~~could~~ watch movies in theaters, rent them, see them on network television, or even buy them.

Life is so different now than it been at the beginning of the twentieth century

that we could hardly imagine how people lived then. For example, now we can see

all the latest movies, watch television, or listen to the radio whenever we want to.

Movies was also popular in the early 1900s, but they were very different from the

modern movies that we could watch. The technology to add sound be not in

existence until the 1920s. Viewers of early movies will read the dialogue in "titles,"

or lines of print on the screen. Unlike movies, radio and television was not in

existence yet in 1900. Although the first radio communication signal had been sent

in 1895 by an Italian inventor named Marconi, the radio as we know it had not yet

being invented. Ship-to-shore radio is operational before there was any radio

stations that can broadcast programs. In fact, many survivors of the *Titanic* probably

will have died in 1912 without radio communication. The first commercial radio

station probably been WWJ, in Detroit, Michigan. It was not until the 1920s that the

average person can enjoy comedies, dramas, music, and soap operas on the radio,

and several decades later before they can watch television every day.

Correcting Errors with Irregular Verbs

Directions: Correct all errors with verbs in the following passage. Cross out the incorrect forms and write the correct forms above the line.

had
Example: During the Great Depression of the 1930s, many people ~~haved~~ a hard time earning a living and supporting their families.

On October 24, 1929, which is knowed as Black Thursday, stock market prices falled sharply, without warning. A few days later, the stock market collapsed. Many investors losed a great deal of money, and businessmen gone broke. Today we could hardly imagine the feeling of panic that swept the country in 1929 and the years that followed. Many thousands of people no longer haved jobs, and they can not provide for their families. By 1933, unemployment had rised to 25%. Even for those who were lucky enough to be working, wages had went down to only 60% of what they were in 1929. Farmers too experienced hard times. They faught against the devastating effects of dust storms. In parts of the Great Plains area, the winds blowed away three to four inches of topsoil and ruined the farmland. Large numbers of farmers and their families losted their land because they can't paid their debts, and they become homeless. Some choose to migrate westward in search of jobs, which were difficult to find.

Using Progressive Tenses

Directions: Choose an appropriate progressive tense of each underlined verb and write it above that verb.

had been looking
Example: We <u>had looked</u> forward to that vacation for months.

The summer after my high school graduation, two friends and I went on a driving trip around California. As we <u>traveled</u> north on Interstate 15, we talked about all the things we would miss about high school, as well as what we <u>expected</u> from our future lives. "By the year 2000, I <u>hope</u> to be a millionaire," announced one of my friends. "You <u>will probably still work</u> at the hamburger store," joked my other friend. "No way," I broke in. "He <u>has planned</u> his get-rich strategy in detail for over a year now. He'll be a millionaire for sure." Being out on the road with no real responsibilities felt great because all three of us <u>had worked</u> many hours per week while we were in high school, and we had college and jobs lined up ahead of us as well. Even though the vacation <u>passed</u> by too quickly, we enjoyed it while we could.

Maintaining Consistency in Tense

Directions: Several sentences in the paragraph below suffer from inconsistency in verb tense. Cross out each error, and write the correct verb form above it.

Example: While we were visiting Chinatown in San Francisco, my uncle Burt

insisted

~~insists~~ on taking us to an Italian restaurant.

San Francisco is one of the highlights of our driving trip around California. San Francisco was a real metropolis, with many activities and a lot of interesting things to see. The first day, we rode on the cable cars, climb Nob Hill to see Coit Tower, drive down twisty Lombard Street on Russian Hill, and buy freshly-steamed crabs and fresh-baked sourdough bread for a picnic dinner in Golden Gate Park. The next day we travel over the Golden Gate Bridge and visited cool and shady Muir Woods with its giant redwood trees, and when we come back we shop for chocolate and souvenirs at Ghirardelli Square and Pier 39. Our third day in the city, we see Little Japan and ate sitting on the floor at a real Japanese restaurant. On the last day, we go to Chinatown, my favorite part of San Francisco, where we saw older Chinese gentlemen reading the newspapers that had been posted in shop windows for that purpose. We notice that they read the Chinese characters from top to bottom, as they gradually bend lower and lower until they come to the bottom of each page, and then straighten up again to read the next line. Next time I go to San Francisco, I

want to see Alcatraz, the museums in Golden Gate Park, and the nearby University

of California at Berkeley.

Using Personal Pronouns Correctly

Directions: Most sentences in the following paragraph contain one or more errors in personal pronoun use. Cross out the incorrect pronouns, and write the correct forms above them.

Example: The nearby community college changed ~~it's~~ *its* registration procedures last semester.

Where does the time go? It seems like only yesterday that me daughter Rachel was starting kindergarten. Now Rachel is taking his first classes at Cuyamaca College this year. Her was somewhat surprised to learn that at her college, students can register for classes by phone. Many students find that this system works better for they because it is so much more convenient than the old method of standing in line at the Admissions and Records Office. One of hers friends, Luke Denly, is also taking classes at the same college. He has already finished more than one year of classes, and he's schedule is quite different from Rachel's. She saw he there for the first time the other day, and he gave she a few tips about being a successful student. I hope this is a successful semester for both he and she.

Using Indefinite Pronouns and Verbs Correctly

Directions: There are several errors involving indefinite pronouns in the paragraph below. Cross out each incorrect pronoun or verb form, and write the corrected form on the line above.

Example: Many brides ~~is~~ *are* choosing Bob Carlisle's *Butterfly Kisses* for the first dance with their fathers, at their wedding receptions.

Most fathers is shocked to see his daughters grow up. Watching a child mature is a difficult passage in life, and its effects are deep. One popular song, Bob Carlisle's *Butterfly Kisses*, sets this theme to music and expresses what many dads feels as each one see his daughter going to kindergarten for the first time, then high school, often college, and in many cases, getting married. Few of the other fathers that I know wants to talk about this topic because it is too emotional. The others prefers to ignore it, or suffer in silence, as they see their role in their daughters' lives changing. None of the fathers that I know has openly acknowledged the bittersweet emotions that come as a result of moving from their traditional role of protector to that of caring bystander, even though most of us has done our best to equip them to be successful and independent adults. Everyone say that fathers aren't as emotional as mothers, but as the father of four daughters, I know that this isn't true, even if we sometimes wish it were. As fathers, we hope that each one of our daughters feel confident enough to make her own way in life, but we also hope that our daughters

will still love us even when they no longer needs us as they did when they were

young.

Using Nouns and Pronouns Correctly

Directions: The following sentences contain errors in the use of nouns and pronouns. Cross out the errors and write the corrections above. Make sure subject nouns agree with their verbs. Finally, make sure the pronoun case is correct.

their
Example: For many young people, college is ~~they~~ first step into the adult world.

My first crises in college came just two weeks into me first semester of class, when me Spanish professor, Dr. Barrera, gave us our first assignments back. My grade was a C-. Me had always done very well in language classes, taking French, Spanish, and German in high school, and I was shocked to see such a low grade in my best subject. I wasn't alone in this; nearly everyone in the class were surprised to see such low grades. After class, I approached the professor and asked he why I had received such a low grade. He told me, "Oh, you Spanish is pretty good, but yours don't know how to write a paragraph." He said that some people expects high school to prepare students for college, but many times their need more help to come up to the level them need to be to succeed in college classes. I asked him if me and him could sit down together and analyze my paragraph to see how I could improve it, and him said that his would be glad to help.   At that time, I realized with a sinking heart that mathematics weren't going to be my hardest class after all.

Using Adjectives and Adverbs Correctly

Directions: Correct all errors in the use of adjectives and adverbs. Draw a line through the error, and write the correct form above the line.

Example: Sheila and Greg thought Introduction to Philosophy was one of the

best
~~bestest~~ classes they had ever taken.

The atmosphere in the philosophy classroom was tensely as the students

waited anxiously for their new professor to arrive. Dr. Roland Wolff, whose

lectures were always real interesting and whose tests were always easily, had retired

very sudden in the middle of the semester. Rumor had it that the day after he

retired, he had taken off quick for a secret destination in the South Pacific, where he

planned to live quietly and comfortable for the rest of his life. He had always lived

the most privatest life of any professor on campus, so it was not real strange or

remarkably that he had gone off by himself. However, he would be greatly missed.

None of the students knew anything about Dr. Quoyle, who had agreed to

take over Dr. Wolff's classes on shortest notice. When his largest frame appeared in

the doorway, they couldn't help but stare. Dr. Quoyle was a very tallest man with

red hair and the most biggest chin they had ever seen. However, after he announced

that he was going to cut two books from the reading list, they began to feel more

better. Maybe they would like Dr. Quoyle after all.

Correcting Double Negatives

Directions: Correct the double negatives in the following paragraph. Draw a line through words that need to be changed and write your revision above the line, or rewrite the paragraph on your own paper if you prefer.

Example: Your auto insurance rates will be lower if you never have *~~no~~ any* accidents.

Zachary kept telling himself that he didn't have no right to be angry. After all, he had been speeding, so he probably deserved the ticket. But he hadn't ever gotten no traffic tickets before, and besides, he didn't know where he was going to get the money to pay for it. He was also afraid that his insurance rates would go up, and he couldn't hardly afford his insurance payments now. He considered asking his parents to loan him the money, but just last week when they had paid for his new tires, his dad had said they wouldn't give him no more money for anything except school. Could he borrow money from his girlfriend? Not hardly, he thought. She never had no money to spare. Then he remembered that his cousin Alex had been interested in buying his guitar, which he really didn't play much no more. Alex would be happy about getting the guitar, and he knew just how he would use the money.

Correcting Errors with Modifiers

Directions: Correct all errors involving incorrect forms of adjectives or adverbs and misplaced or dangling *-ing* modifiers. Cross out each error and write the correct form or correct phrase above the line. In some cases, you may need to rewrite an entire sentence or clause.

Example: I saw a rattlesnake ~~riding my bicycle in a remote area~~.

Corrected: *Riding my bicycle in a remote area, I saw a rattlesnake.*

Before the young campers arrived, the campground seemed quietly and peacefully. As a real new camp counselor, I was eager to look around the area, so I started to explore. I saw ground squirrels and lizards hiking along the trails. The most biggest crow that I had ever seen scolded me loudly sitting in a tree. Jumping out of the lake, I saw several fish, and a few wild ducks were swimming slow and graceful. I imagined the real enthusiastic youngsters paddling canoes wearing orange life vests. Then, blowing across the water, I noticed the wind, and the lake began to look most dangerous than it had before. Soon rain started coming down hard, and my clothes were completely soaked. Approaching one of the cabins, I decided to go inside and take shelter from the storm that had begun so quick.

Correcting Errors in Agreement with Indefinite Pronouns

Directions: Cross out each error, and then write the correction above it. Change the verb if necessary. More than one correct answer may be possible.

their
Example: Many students have different goals for ~~his or her~~ college experience.

Each student has
or: ~~Many students have~~ a different goal for his or her college experience.

In today's higher education, not every college student fits the stereotypical image of the full-time scholar who is determined to receive their traditional four-year degree in the shortest time possible. While many college students still have a degree as his or her goal, others are taking shorter courses of study to prepare themselves for a career. In addition, someone who has a full-time job may register for classes in math, writing, or their chosen field in order to improve the chances of getting a promotion. Finally, many college classes have a few students who are studying for personal or family reasons, such as sheer love of learning, learning a foreign language for travel, or improving their basic skills in order to help his or her children with their homework. All of these students have their own goals and reasons to study in college, and each college should give him the welcome he deserves. Everyone who is willing to study hard in college classes needs our full support and encouragement, no matter what their goals are.

Correcting Unclear or Ambiguous Pronoun References

Directions: Cross out each unclear or ambiguous pronoun reference, and then write a correction above it. Change the verb if necessary. More than one correct answer may be possible.

Example: Non-traditional college students should investigate sources of help for ~~it~~ **college**.

Many colleges offer programs for non-traditional students, and in recent years, a number of students have taken advantage of them. At many colleges, evening and weekend college programs provide an opportunity for those who cannot attend school Monday through Friday during the day because of their full-time jobs or family responsibilities. At some colleges, an older or "re-entry" student may be able to see a special counselor if she needs help to learn about college programs and resources. Extra tutoring may also be available to students who need help with a content class or basic writing or math skills, and it can mean the difference between getting a good grade in a class or dropping out. A large number of colleges now have special resource centers for returning female students. They can help make arrangements for such necessities as orientation to the college, childcare, and career choices. Investigating all the resources that are available can make it easier.

Correcting Problems with Pronouns

Directions: Proofread the following paragraph for problems with pronoun-antecedent agreement and sexist language. Make any necessary changes by crossing out the incorrect word and writing a more effective choice above it. More than one correct answer may be possible.

Example: Many colleges have a website where students can look up information

the college programs and services.
about ~~it~~.

When a first-time college student arrives on campus, he often has no idea of

the many resources available to assist him with his studies. Each student has to go

through the same process of discovering everything they can about their new

college. Whether a student is studying for a profession such as policeman or

businessman, or taking classes for personal or professional enrichment, they can

benefit from the many programs available on college campuses today. Students

who invest some time and energy investigating the college facilities, including

recreational facilities and programs, financial aid and scholarships, and tutoring and

counseling services, will find that these are worth the effort. Before one of my

friends started classes, another friend and herself went to the campus to become

familiar with some of the services, and that helped her feel much more comfortable

on the first day of classes. Students who take this advice will get the most from his

or her college experience.

Using Parallel Words in a Series

Directions: Several sentences in the following paragraph contain errors in parallelism. Cross out the errors, and write the correct version above the faulty one, if necessary.

Example: Our college offers classes in swimming, running, soccer, baseball, and ~~to learn~~ racquetball.

Regular exercise is valuable to reduce stress, increase general health, and extending a person's lifespan. More specifically, exercise improves cardio-respiratory fitness, muscular strength, muscular endurance, flexibility, and your body composition becomes healthier. Whether you choose to lift weights, participate in a physical education class, take up a martial art, join a team, or just walking or running regularly, exercise can give you a happier life. Other options for the more adventurous include kayaking, biking, or a mountain climb. Whichever option you choose, be sure to begin gradually and working up to more strenuous levels over time, or you run the risk of injury.

Using Parallel Structure with Phrases

Directions: Several sentences in the following paragraph contain errors in parallelism. Cross out the errors, and write the correct version above the faulty one, if necessary.

Example: Their family vacation in Hawaii included snorkeling in the bay, hiking

playing

into an extinct volcano, and ~~they played~~ golf on a beautiful course.

Many interesting recreational activities such as nature walks, group bicycle rides, stargazing, or going to a lecture on art and history are available in most communities, but they are not always well-advertised or you can't find them easily. One good source of information is the local newspaper. One day per week, many local newspapers offer a column on "What's Happening" at area galleries, museums, parks, and from sports facilities. Another rich source of information on local events is the Internet. Local sites such as "Sign On San Diego" or "Digital City Philadelphia" carry a wealth of information on regional events and activities, and if you have America Online, to click on the "Local" channel. These recreational events can provide you with the opportunity of meeting new people and the chance to participate in interesting and fun activities.

Maintaining Parallelism

Directions: Check the sentences in the following paragraph for errors in parallelism. Cross out each incorrect form, and write your correction in the space above.

Example: Experts recommend that we eat a variety of types of vegetables and fruits

every day in order to get a sufficient number of necessary nutrients, or *that we take* ~~taking~~ a

multi-vitamin tablet.

Good health involves eating well, exercising regularly, getting enough sleep, and have a good social life. Most recent nutritional guidelines state that a minimum of five servings of fruits and vegetables per day are recommended; excessive sugar, refined flour, and eating a lot of fat should be avoided; and you should consume an adequate amount of water. People should also exercise at least three times per week for 30 minutes or more each time, and to keep track of their heart rate so that it stays between 50% and 70% of their maximum rate. Ideally, getting enough sleep means not only to wake up naturally, without relying on an alarm clock, but also going to bed early enough to feel rested in the morning. Finally, being in daily contact with family or close friends has been shown to extend the average lifespan. If you want to be at the peak of health, you should try to incorporate good nutrition, regular exercise, get sufficient rest, and enjoy personal relationships into your daily life.

Correct Spelling of Words with Suffixes

Directions: Check for correct spelling in words ending with the suffixes *-able*, *-al*, *-ed*, *-ful*, *-ing*, *-ive*, *-ly*, *-ment*, and *-tion*. Cross out each incorrect form, and write the correct version above it.

Example: It is possible for some students who have never ~~graduateed~~ *graduated* from high

school to ~~successfuly~~ *successfully* attend college.

A college educateion is more expenseive now than ever before, but a little

resourcefullnes in researching financial aid can make it more afforddable. While

some occupations require a special talent or practical experience, statistics show that

students who have graduatted from college are earnning, on average, much more

than students who have only a high school diploma. Even takeing a few college

courses can increase your earnings, but college is expenseive. The average cost for a

year of college is over $6500, including educationall expenses and room and board.

Private colleges cost much more, but they also offer more financeial aid; in fact, at

many colleges, almost every student receives at least some financial aid, whether in

the form of scholarships, loans, grants, or work/study jobs. If you are hopeing or

planing to attend college, a careful investigashun of sources of help at a local library

or on the Internet may realy pay off. Finaly, use good judgment in your financial

arrangments. If you pay income taxes, you can even get a tax credit for part of your

costs, and you can save money by liveing at home and attendding a nearby college.

Using Commonly Confused and Commonly Misspelled Words

Directions: Check for correct spelling and usage in the following paragraph. Cross out each incorrect form, and write the correct version above it.

> *advise*   *exceeds*
>
> Example: Experts ~~advice~~ not taking on a debt that ~~exeedes~~ your ability to repay.

A morgage is kind of loan used to purchase real estate, such as a house or condominium. Most morgages must be paid off over a period of 15 to 40 years, and if the homebuyer stops paying, the agency or individual whom lent the money can take the house and sell it in order to pay off the remaining debt. Each time a payment is made, part of the money is credited to interest and the rest is credited to the principle, which is the original amount of money that was borrowed. There are many financial advantages to buying a home instead of renting, and at least too disadvantages. One advantage is that when interest rates are low, buyers can sometimes buy a property for fewer then it would cost to rent a similar property, and its possible to lock in a fixed payment that will never go up in the future. In addition, the U.S. government generaly permits morgage borrowers to deduct the interest they pay on their home loan from their income taxes. On the negative side, homeowners must pay state and local property taxes and all the costs to maintane and repair their homes. If your in the market for a home, a good stragety is to get good advise before you sign any papers, and be sure to shop around for the best

interest rates and the lowest loan fees. If you now the basic facts about a morgage,

you will enjoy the benifits for many years.

Using Correct Spelling

Directions: Cross out each misspelled word in the following paragraph and write the corrected version above.

ceiling
Example: Some analysts say that stock prices are approaching a ~~cieling~~ while others say

there
~~their~~ is still room for growth.

Fourty percent of all households are now investing in the stock market threw

mutual funds, and in the last decade stock ownership has risen 46 percent between

households earning fewer than $50,000. Many middle-class wage earners now

beleive that the stock market guarantees a better rate of return than traditionnal

savings accounts. While prudent stock investors often succede over the long run,

in the short term, its possible to loose money even on conservative stock

investments if overall stock prices fall in response to any number of possible crisises

around the world. Experts agree that investors shouldn't let greed supercede their

need to make wise investments, and no one should gamble that stock market

indexes will rise over any short period of time. Perhaps the best strategy for

investting wisely is to follow the experts' advise and learn as much as possible about

a company or fund before commiting your hard-earned cash.

Using Commas in a Series

Directions: Add commas where they are needed in several series in the paragraph below. Other commas are already provided.

Example: *Yahoo, Webcrawler, Dogpile,* and *Ask Jeeves* are examples of the many different search engines available on the Internet.

There is such a large quantity of information available on the Internet these days that it is becoming very difficult to find the exact information we need. People looking for information about a baseball team's schedule may have to wade through vast amounts of local news financial disclosures or player statistics before they hit on the team's home page, and when I recently looked up podiatry osteopathy dentistry and chiropractic, I was overwhelmed with information that I didn't need. Fortunately, there are some strategies that can help searchers find what they are looking for. These include using advanced search features multi-engine searches or plain English searches. Advanced features permit a searcher to specify exact phrases that must be included, as well as words or phrases that must not be included, while multi-engine searches like *Dogpile Mamma* and *SavvySearch* allow the user to search several sites at the same time. Plain English searches such as *Ask Jeeves* allow the searcher to type in a question in plain English. Using one of these strategies the next time you are searching for information on the Internet may help you find the information you want.

Using Commas with Conjunctions and Nonrestrictive Elements

Directions: Add commas where they are needed with conjunctions and nonrestrictive elements in the paragraph below.

Example: Science fiction includes a wide variety of stories, *but* most people have read only one or two styles of science fiction.

Science fiction books and movies have become very popular in recent years. Most science fiction falls into four categories—hard science fiction, science fantasy (also known as sword and sorcery), speculative fiction, and genre science fiction. While hard science fiction features such possible technological advancements as interstellar travel or death rays speculative fiction focuses more on the nature of possible future societies. Although story lines in science fantasy are often modeled after romantic stories of knights in shining armor some science fantasy can be quite original. Genre science fiction which includes the popular *Star Trek* stories takes place in pre-defined but somewhat flexible settings and involves familiar characters and locations, such as Captain Kirk and the Starship *Enterprise*. One recent style of science fiction, cyberpunk, combines elements from several of these categories to portray the interaction of the human mind with computers and these stories often include a street-wise hero or heroes.

Using Commas Correctly

Directions: Add commas where they are needed in the paragraph below.

Example: Cable companies, *once limited to providing television service,* are now expanding their offerings into the telephone market.

In addition to cable television many cable companies are now offering phone service and high-speed Internet access over their fiber-optic cable networks. Lower rates wider no-fee calling areas and faster Internet connections have motivated large numbers of phone customers to switch carriers as these services become available in new areas. Customers may even keep their old phone numbers; however traditional phone companies have begun charging a fee for number portability. Pacific Bell for example currently charges ten dollars to transfer a phone number to another company. Things have changed since the 1970s when one famous television comedian playing the role of a telephone operator said "We don't care. We don't have to. We're the phone company."

Using Quotation Marks

Directions: Add quotation marks where they are needed in the paragraph below.

Example: Bob Dylan's Blowin' In the Wind is still one of my favorite songs.

Correct: Bob Dylan's *"Blowin' In the Wind"* is still one of my favorite songs.

How long have you been a student at this college? I asked the person sitting

next to me on the first day of a music appreciation class. Two years, he replied, and

then asked me if I had heard anything about the class. Yes, and I am a little nervous,

I answered him. I've heard that we study everything from classical music like

Bach's Christmas Oratorio and Mozart's Eine Kleine Nachtmusik to gospel, rhythm

and blues, and modern types of rock music like rap, techno, and punk, I continued,

but I'm nervous about the tests. No problem, my classmate insisted, you can check

out all the tapes from the library. That's a relief, and thanks for the encouragement,

I whispered to him as music started to play and the teacher approached the podium.

Using Apostrophes

Directions: Add apostrophes where they are needed in the paragraph below.

Example: Toms and Kathleens bikes both need to be adjusted.
Corrected: *Tom's* and *Kathleen's* bikes both need to be adjusted.

One of my favorite activities is riding a mountain bike on nearby paths and trails. My bike works well even though its a few years old. My bike isnt as fancy as my friends bike, but it gets the job done. My friend Louis Carrillos bike has more features, like front suspension and V-brakes, but my bikes frame is stronger and it has decent components too. Both bikes tires are designed for off-road riding, and we carry patch kits to repair any flats we get. Both are mens bikes, with high top bars on the frames. My favorite place to ride is in the Laguna Mountains, although I dont have as much time to ride as I did when I was younger. If you decide to take up riding, make sure to wear a helmet and gloves to protect yourself in a crash, because one day youll be thankful you have them.

Using Semicolons, Colons, and Capitalization

Directions: Add semicolons and colons where they are needed in the paragraph below, and correct any mistakes in capitalization.

Example: we landed in buenos aires, argentina, for three reasons the weather was bad, the crew had the flu, and the fuel was getting low it was an exciting trip.

Correct: *We* landed in *Buenos Aires, Argentina,* for three *reasons: the* weather was bad, the crew had the flu, and the fuel was getting *low; it* was an exciting trip.

one of the most exciting experiences in my life was traveling to uruguay in

south america from june 5, 1973, through the end of august. i stayed with a family

of four mamá, papá, guillermo, and gaby. they had an older sister, michelle she was

already married and living with her husband. papá was a t.v. and radio announcer.

the schools were closed at that time, so the young people spent every day walking

around the city and talking about everything we could think of life, relationships,

the future, and religion. one of the most interesting features in the city was el cerro,

which means "the hill." it was the only real hill in montevideo at the top we had

an amazing view of the city. someday i hope to take my own children on a trip like

that one.